Become a mightier writer with CGP!

This CGP book is perfect for helping Year 4 pupils improve their writing —
it's packed with guided activities based on a wide range of styles and genres,
plus 'extra challenge' questions to get them writing independently.

Answers to every question are included in a cut-out-and-keep section,
so it's easy to keep track of how pupils are getting on.

You can also download free annotated examples of a range of text types
to give pupils ideas for their own writing. You'll find them here:

www.cgpbooks.co.uk/KS2WritingResources

What CGP is all about

Our sole aim here at CGP is to produce the highest quality books
— carefully written, immaculately presented and
dangerously close to being funny.

Then we work our socks off to get them out to you
— at the cheapest possible prices.

Contents

The exercises in this book cover different types of writing, and different techniques you can use to make your writing effective. Use the contents below to see what's covered where.

Published by CGP

Editors: Catherine Heygate, Katya Parkes, Hannah Roscoe
Contributors: Samantha Bensted, Alison Griffin, Amanda MacNaughton, Maxine Petrie
With thanks to Claire Boulter and Maxine Petrie for the proofreading.
With thanks to Emily Smith for the copyright research.

ISBN: 978 1 78294 955 8

Thumb illustration used throughout the book © iStock.com.
Images and clipart throughout the book from Corel® and clipart.com
Printed by Elanders Ltd, Newcastle upon Tyne.
Based on the classic CGP style created by Richard Parsons.

Planning Your Writing

Before you start writing, you need to plan your work — this includes thinking about the purpose and audience. The purpose and audience of your text affect the language you use — e.g. a report for adults might be formal and factual.

Planning also includes thinking about how to structure your writing — e.g. how to start and end your text, what order your ideas should come in.

Key Terms

- The <u>purpose</u> of a text is the reason why it's been written.

- e.g. to entertain, to persuade, to inform, to discuss

- The <u>audience</u> is the person or people who read a piece of writing.

- e.g. a letter for parents, a leaflet for teenagers

1 Here are some ideas for different texts. Think about what the main purpose of each text would be. Colour the texts that would entertain in blue and the texts that would inform in red.

A script for a school play about a daring pirate adventure

An article explaining new train ticket prices in the region

An explanation in a textbook about how waterfalls form

A fantasy story about a mischievous elf who tricks humans

A poem about a day at the circus

A mystery story about the case of Mrs Simm's stolen wheelbarrow

Instructions on how to get to the city centre from the airport

(2) **The extracts below are from two different texts about how chocolate is made.**

1. Do you know how yummy chocolate is made? Read on to find out about the magic behind this scrumptious treat.

2. Chocolate is made from cocoa beans, which are native to regions with humid, tropical climates, such as Central America.

Which extract do you think was written for adults? Explain your answer.

I think that extract .... was written for adults

because ....

....

(3) **Draw lines to match each text to the most appropriate style of writing.**

A leaflet encouraging children to walk to school

Language that builds suspense, short sentences

A mystery story set on a deserted island

First person, chatty language

A diary entry about what you did at the weekend

Persuasive language, commands

What features should a report on the benefits of owning a pet include? Circle two options.

Serious tone   Jokes

Direct speech   Facts and figures

(4) Read these extracts from a report on the Vikings in Britain.
Circle the extract that comes from the report's introduction.

If you'd like to find out more about the Vikings in Britain, there are several great resources online.

Around AD 790, ships full of raiding warriors landed on British shores. The Vikings had arrived.

Below are three other topics to go in the report.
Number them from 1-3 to put them in the most logical order.

What did the Vikings do while they were in Britain? ....

Why did the Vikings first come to Britain? ....

When and why did the Vikings leave? ....

(5) Fill in the gaps to complete the plan for this story.
You can use the questions and picture below to help you.

1. Beginning — Scott volunteers to take part in a trick at a magic show.

2. The spell goes wrong! He ....
....

3. Desperate for a cure, he goes to ....
....

4. To reverse the spell he must ....
....

5. End — ....
....

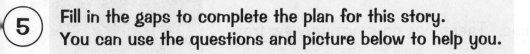

"I can plan fiction and non-fiction texts."

Editing Your Work

Every piece of writing you do needs to be edited. This means reading it carefully to check whether it makes sense and if you could make it better.

You can make your writing better by removing unnecessary words, as well as by splitting or combining sentences.

> Reading your work aloud can help you see how it could be improved.

(1) This is a passage from a piece of writing about a trip on the London Eye. Some of the words in the extract don't give the reader any new information. Read the extract, then cross out any words that aren't needed.

The wheel turned slowly as we slowly rose higher

above the skyline. There was an amazing view from

the top and it was incredible! I could see people in

the streets scurrying around like ants in the streets.

My mum took lots of photos, so I brought some

photos my mum took into school to show my friends.

(2) These extracts are from a historical story about the Romans. Rewrite each extract to make it better.

> Think about whether you need to split the sentences up or combine them.

The soldier had been marching for hours and he was tired

and sore and he wanted to rest but he still had miles to go.

....

....

He had blisters on his toes. He had blisters on his heels.

....

(3) This is an extract from a fantasy story about a unicorn.
Some suggestions have been written on it in red.
Read the extract, and then read the suggestions.

These two sentences could be combined.
Monty crept silently forwards. He was moving towards the unicorn.

Suddenly, it bolted into the forest, leaving a trail
These words aren't needed.
of glitter behind it as it ran through the forest.

Monty sprinted through the trees, desperately trying
Shorten this sentence by changing the comma to a full stop.
to keep up, eventually exhaustion forced him to stop
These words aren't needed.
because he was tired. He watched as the unicorn vanished into the darkness.

Rewrite the extract, using the suggestions to make it better.

....

....

....

....

....

Read the original extract, then
the text you have written.
Which one is clearer? Why?

....

(4) This is an extract from an article persuading people to stop littering. Read
the extract, then write on it any changes that are needed to make it better.

Litter is unsightly. Litter can harm wildlife. Animals can become trapped in litter

or swallow it if they think it's food, or they can get stuck in it, so this means that

it's very important to put litter in the bin instead of throwing litter on the ground.

"I can edit my work to make it better."

Section 1 — Drafting Your Work

Proofreading Your Work

When you've finished editing your writing, you should proofread it.
This means looking for mistakes in spelling, punctuation and grammar,
as well as any places where the writing isn't clear.

1 This is a late draft of a report about snow leopards.
Read it carefully. Circle each mistake and write the
correction above it. The first one has been done for you.

There are 12 more mistakes for you to find in the text.

The snow leopard is a species of large cat that ~~are~~ *is* found in Asia. It lives in

mountainous areas like the Himalayas, where the landscape is rockey and the

temperature is well low. Snow leopads

have thick fur to keep them warm, and their

patterned coat allows them to blend in with

there surroundings. They also have big

fury paws that help them to walk on snow.

Unlike lions and tigers. snow leopards can't raw — instead, they communicate

in hisses and growls?

Unfortunately, there were lots of threats to snow leopards. Global warming

is changing their habitat: making it difficult for them to find food. In addition,

they are often hunted for their beautyful coats. However, there is hope for

the species. Many countries in Asia are trying to save the snow leopard by

protecting it's habitat and educating the public.

"I can proofread my work and correct mistakes."

A Letter to a Friend

If you're writing to someone you know well, like a friend or a member of your family, you don't usually want it to sound too formal. Instead, it should be informal and personal — like you're having a conversation.

Key Terms

Formal writing has a serious tone. It often uses complex language.

e.g. Some found the food acceptable. Others felt it was absolutely dreadful.

Informal writing is more friendly and personal. It often uses chatty language.

e.g. I thought that the food was OK. My mate didn't like it at all though.

1 The box at the bottom of the page contains some different ways of starting and finishing a letter. Work out which ones are formal and which are informal and write them in the correct column in the table.

Formal	Informal

See you soon	Dear Sir	Yours faithfully	Loads of love
	To whom it may concern		Best regards
Hi	Love and hugs	Yours sincerely	Hello

2 Some of the sentences below are informal and others are formal. Colour the informal sentences in red and the formal sentences in blue.

> We took tonnes of great photos!

> The country roads were well bumpy.

> We paused to enjoy some delicious snacks.

> It was boiling — we couldn't believe how sunny it was.

> I went on a bicycle ride with my friends.

> I am disappointed that you were unable to attend.

★ **Extra Challenge**

Rewrite all of the formal sentences to make them informal instead.

3 Here is an extract from a letter to a friend. Underline all the examples of formal language.

My mother informed me that you will be visiting us next month. I am extremely excited about seeing you. We can go on an excursion to the new theme park in my area. I have

© bukharova/ iStock Editorial/ Getty Images Plus

heard that it is thoroughly enjoyable, despite the queues for the rides being rather long. We may also travel into the city in order to visit the shoe shop I was speaking to you about. Recently, I purchased some wellington boots there.

Rewrite the extract from the previous page, changing the language to make it informal.

> Think about the words and phrases you'd use if you were talking to a friend.

....

....

....

....

....

(4) Imagine you're on holiday. Write a postcard to a relative at home using informal language.

> Where are you? What have you done while you've been there?

> What has been your favourite part of the holiday? Why?

> You should use an informal greeting and sign-off.

....

....

....

....

....

....

....

★ Extra Challenge

Rewrite your postcard, changing the language to make it formal.

....

....

....

"I can make my writing informal."

A Day at a Country Show

When you're writing about something that happened to you, you need to describe your experience clearly and in chronological order. Describe the event from your point of view (in the first person) and use the past tense.

Key Terms

- The <u>first person</u> is used to write from the point of view of the writer.

  e.g. I took our dog for a walk.

- The <u>past tense</u> is used to write about things that have already happened.

  e.g. We went to Ireland for our holiday last year.

- <u>Chronological order</u> is when events are organised in the order they occur.

  e.g. I played on the swings with my friends. It started to rain, so we ran home.

1 This is an extract from a diary entry about a day trip to a country show. Fill in the gaps with the correct form of the verb in brackets so that the passage is in the past tense. The first one has been done for you.

Last weekend, I (**to go**) .... went .... to a country show in Somerset.

We (**to arrive**) .... a bit late, so I (**to have**) ....

to hurry to get to the first event — the children's show jumping competition.

I (**to run**) .... to the arena

and (**to find**) .... a seat just

in time. I (**to be**) .... so

excited that I (**to hold**) ....

my breath as the first pony (**to trot**)

.... into the arena.

2 Diary entries should use the first person. Rewrite this extract about a bird of prey display at the country show in the first person.

He'd never seen a bird of prey up close before. He held the owl gently on his arm as she peered at him with her bright orange eyes. He was quite scared at first, but he was proud of himself for staying calm.

....

....

....

....

....

3 This extract has been scrambled up, so the events aren't in the right order. Rewrite the extract, putting the sentences in chronological order.

Read the original extract and the version you've written. Which one is clearer? Why?

Then, I washed the custard off my face and went to watch the tractor race.

After seeing the birds of prey, I took part in the custard pie-throwing contest.

Later, I went to the results ceremony for the giant vegetable competition —

it was the perfect way to end the day.

....

....

....

....

....

4 Think about a new skill you've learned recently. Write a description of how you learned the skill. Make sure you use the first person and the past tense, and write in chronological order.

What was the first step in learning the skill?

What did you have to do next?

What was the final step? Did you achieve something?

The skill could be anything you've learned — either at school or at home.

....

....

....

....

....

....

....

....

....

....

....

★ **Extra Challenge**

Write a diary entry about what you did at the weekend. Make sure that you put the things you did in chronological order.

"I can use the first person and the past tense to write about things that I have done."

My Recipe Book

Instructions **tell** you how to do something — for example, how to make a cake. Instructions should always be clear and easy to follow.

It's really important that instructions are in the right order, so that the reader knows exactly when they should carry out each step in the process. Adding extra details to your points can make your instructions more helpful too.

1 This is an **extract** from a recipe for making a rainbow birthday cake. The points have been mixed up so that they're in the wrong order. Read each point, then write the numbers in the correct order below.

1. Split the cake mix between seven bowls and add a different colour to each one.

2. Put the sugar and butter in a bowl and mix them together.

3. Bake each cake for 15 minutes.

4. Sieve the flour, then add it to the sugar, butter and eggs. Stir gently.

5. Start by weighing out the ingredients.

6. Once the butter and sugar are mixed, add the eggs.

....

What do you think the next two steps in the recipe will be?

The photo above might give you some ideas.

1. ....

2. ....

Section 2 — Writing Non-Fiction

2 Fill in the gaps in this recipe for chocolate icing, giving an **extra detail** about each step.

1. For this recipe you'll need 120ml of double cream and 220g of chocolate (..................
....).

Is it better if a certain kind of chocolate is used?

2. Bring the cream to the boil — ....
....

What might happen if the cream gets too hot?

3. Pour the hot cream over the chocolate and
stir ....
....

How should the icing look when it's ready?

3 The pictures below show the process for making buttercream icing.
Write out the instructions in full, using the words in the box to help you.

| beat | icing sugar | weighing scales | mixing bowl | butter |

1. ....

2. ....

3. ....

4 Write some instructions for making a sandwich with three of your favourite fillings. Make sure your points are in a sensible order. Include extra details to make your points easier to understand.

What is the first step in the instructions? Do you need to butter the bread?

What equipment will you need to make the sandwich?

Are there any extra details that would help the reader? What type of bread works best? How much of each filling is needed?

Do any fillings need to be prepared? Do you need to grate cheese or slice tomatoes?

1. ....

....

2. ....

....

3. ....

....

4. ....

....

5. ....

....

....

⭐ **Extra Challenge**

Write some instructions for making a snowman. Make sure you put the points in a sensible order.

"I can order my points in instructions and add extra details to them."

How Butterflies Develop

Using a variety of sentence lengths and structures will help to make your writing more interesting.

You can use linking words to vary the length of your sentences. You can also add fronted adverbials to make your sentences more detailed.

Grammar Guide

- Linking words can join clauses or sentences together.

  e.g. The king was hungry but he didn't have any snacks with him.

- An adverbial is a word (or group of words) which describes a verb. It tells us why, when, where or how something happens.

  e.g. He rode back to his kingdom as quickly as possible.

- A fronted adverbial is an adverbial which comes at the start of a sentence.

  e.g. On his way back to the castle, the king went shopping for snacks.

1 Some pairs of sentences from a text explaining the life cycle of a butterfly have been mixed up. Draw lines to match each pair, using one of the linking words to join them together.

> You should only use each linking word once.

| Butterfly eggs are often round. | when | They can also be shaped like cylinders. |

| You have to look carefully to find butterfly eggs. | because | They are ready to hatch. |

| Different butterflies always choose certain plants. | although | They are deciding where to lay their eggs. |

| The eggs remain on the plant. | until | They are extremely small. |

2 This extract explains the next stage of a butterfly's life cycle. Circle the correct option from the linking words in bold to join the clauses together.

The butterfly egg eventually hatches a couple of weeks or months **once / after** it was laid. However, you'll be disappointed **if / though** you were expecting a butterfly to

emerge from the egg. Instead, it is a caterpillar that crawls free.

The caterpillar begins to eat the plants around it **until / as soon as** it hatches. It grows very quickly **unless / because** it eats such a huge amount. In fact, a caterpillar grows so fast **that / although** it has to shed its skin several times throughout its life.

3 Fronted adverbials can help to add detail to an explanation. Fill each gap in this extract with a fronted adverbial from the box below. Don't repeat any of the options.

...., a caterpillar turns into a pod-like

structure called a cocoon. ...., the

caterpillar gradually transforms into a colourful butterfly. ....

..................................., the butterfly crawls free.

> Several weeks later   As often as possible   When it is fully grown
>
>   On some leaves   Inside the cocoon

4 The picture below shows how a dragon develops. Write a step-by-step explanation of the different stages in a dragon's life cycle. Use fronted adverbials and linking words to add detail and variety to your writing.

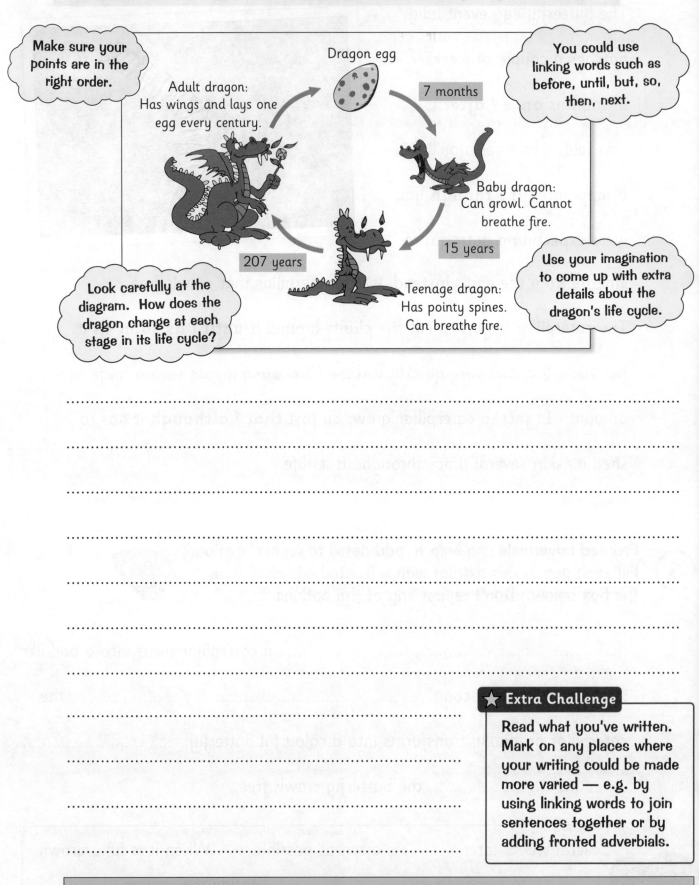

Make sure your points are in the right order.

Dragon egg

7 months

You could use linking words such as before, until, but, so, then, next.

Adult dragon: Has wings and lays one egg every century.

Baby dragon: Can growl. Cannot breathe fire.

207 years

15 years

Look carefully at the diagram. How does the dragon change at each stage in its life cycle?

Teenage dragon: Has pointy spines. Can breathe fire.

Use your imagination to come up with extra details about the dragon's life cycle.

....

....

....

....

....

....

....

★ **Extra Challenge**

Read what you've written. Mark on any places where your writing could be made more varied — e.g. by using linking words to join sentences together or by adding fronted adverbials.

....

....

....

"I can write using detailed and varied sentences."

Save Our Playground!

If you want to convince your reader to agree with you and share your point of view, then you need to make sure your writing is really persuasive.

Statements, commands and rhetorical questions are three techniques that you can use to make your writing as persuasive as possible.

Grammar Guide

- **Statements** are sentences that provide information.

  e.g. Broccoli is very good for you.

- **Commands** are sentences that give instructions or orders.

  e.g. Eat all of your broccoli.

- **Rhetorical questions** ask about something, but they don't need an answer.

  e.g. Who doesn't love tucking in to a big bowl of broccoli?

(1) Here is an extract from an article in a local newsletter. Underline a statement in blue, a rhetorical question in green and a command in red.

Everyone knows how important the playground is to our community.

However, the local council are planning to close it. Isn't that ridiculous?

Sign our petition today to help prevent this happening! Hundreds of families

enjoy the playground every week. It's a popular and friendly place for

children to have fun. Where

else will they play? What about

their safety and happiness?

Help us fight this terrible proposal.

Make your voice heard!

2 Turn these statements into rhetorical questions. You can use the question starters in the box below to help you.

You can change the wording of the statements.

> Who can deny...?
>
> Shouldn't...?
>
> Don't you think...?
>
> Isn't it...?

It's time to put a stop to this plan.

....

Children should be encouraged to play outside.

....

The playground is a great place for children to exercise.

....

....

3 Here are some more extracts from the newsletter article. Turn each statement into a command.

Commands can make your writing more persuasive — they tell the reader to do something.

You could tell all your friends about our campaign.

....

Everyone could write to the council and complain.

....

We would like you to come to the community meeting next week.

....

④ Imagine you are running for a school council which will work to improve your school. Write an article for the school paper that will convince other pupils to vote for you. Remember to use statements, commands and rhetorical questions to make your writing persuasive.

Use commands to tell the reader what you want them to do.

Why should people vote for you? What skills do you have?

Use statements to say what you would do if you got onto the council. How would you improve your school?

You could use the question starters on page 22 to help you write some rhetorical questions.

As your school councillor, I will work hard to make the changes we all want.

....

....

....

....

....

....

....

....

....

....

....

★ Extra Challenge

Swap your work with a partner. Pick out three ways in which it's persuasive and suggest three ways it could be made more persuasive.

"I can use statements, commands and rhetorical questions to write persuasively."

Summer Holidays

You can create **vivid** descriptions by using language which appeals to the senses (touch, taste, sight, smell and sound). Techniques like **similes** and **metaphors** will also help the reader imagine the scenes you are describing.

Key Terms

- <u>Appeals to the senses</u> are descriptions of sight, sound, touch, taste or smell.

  e.g. The delicious aroma of exotic spices wafted through the air.

- A <u>simile</u> describes one thing as being similar to another. Similes often use the words 'like' and 'as'.

  e.g. The city centre was as busy as a beehive.

- A <u>metaphor</u> describes something by saying it is something else.

  e.g. The crowd was a wave, surging towards the shopping centre.

1 Here are some similes and metaphors from a diary entry describing the start of a summer holiday. Colour the similes in red and the metaphors in blue.

> The road was a ribbon stretching out into the distance.

> Fields lay like a patchwork quilt as far as the eye could see.

> It was the hottest day of the year and the car was a furnace.

> The picnic basket was a treasure chest of delicious snacks.

> Cooped up in the car, I grew as restless as a storm.

> The traffic was crawling along like an exhausted tortoise.

2 The photo below was stuck into the diary. Fill in the blanks in the sentences to create similes that describe the photo. The first one has been done for you.

The lighthouse towered over the

beach like ....a soldier, watching....

...over the coastline.............

The sea was as ....

as ....

The rocks were as ....

as ....

The path wound up the hill like

....

3 This is another extract from the diary. Underline the descriptions which appeal to the senses in this extract. The first one has been done for you.

Remember, the senses are touch, taste, sight, smell and sound.

The <u>birds were chirping</u> as I set out. The breeze swept across my

face, ruffling my hair and carrying with it the sweet smell of wild

flowers. Mud squelched under my boots as I made my way into

the woods. I paused for a moment, running my hands over

the rough, gnarled bark of a tree and

listening to its leaves rustling above me.

How do the appeals to the senses make you feel? Do you think they make the text better?

4 This extract is about going swimming in the sea. Fill in the blanks below to make the sentences appeal to the senses. The first one has been done for you.

I raced down the beach and into

the sea. As the waves splashed my

face, I could taste ....the sharp..........

.....saltiness of the water.................

Floating on my back, I listened to the .... sound of

.... all around me.

I swam closer to the shore. Beneath the water, I could feel ....

....

5 Write a description of your favourite place, using similes, metaphors and language which appeals to the senses to make your writing as vivid as possible.

> Similes describe one thing as being similar to another. Metaphors describe something by saying it is something else.

....

....

....

....

★ Extra Challenge

Swap your work with a partner. Underline one simile or metaphor in their work that you find really effective. Explain to them why you think it's so effective.

....

....

....

....

....

"I can use similes, metaphors and appeals to the senses to write effective descriptions."

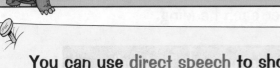
The Hare and the Tortoise

You can use direct speech to show what characters in your stories are saying. Including direct speech in your writing makes the reader feel more involved in the story and helps them to get to know the characters.

Instead of using 'said' when you write speech, try to include a variety of verbs to show how the characters are speaking, e.g. cried, gasped, called.

Grammar Guide

- Direct speech is the words a character says. It goes in inverted commas. It usually starts with a capital letter and always ends with a punctuation mark.

e.g. "Where's the mouse?" asked Mia. "It ran under the bookcase!" shrieked Oliver.

(1) This is the start of a fable called 'The Hare and the Tortoise'. Fill in the gaps with what you think the characters might be saying.

A fable is a story, usually with animal characters, that has a moral. A moral is a lesson that you can learn from a story.

The hare was watching the tortoise amble along.

He couldn't believe how slowly the tortoise moved.

"..

....," he teased.

The tortoise knew he wasn't that slow. He thought of a way to prove it.

"..

...............................," he suggested confidently.

"...

................................!" laughed the hare.

> What do you think the tortoise suggests? Does he want to race the hare? Do you think the hare agrees?

2 You can use verbs other than 'said' to show how a character says something. The headings below all describe how a character might speak. Write down three suitable verbs under each heading.

happily	sadly	quietly	loudly
chuckled	sobbed	murmured	roared

3 Fill in the gaps in the extract below. Instead of using 'said', choose suitable verbs to show how the characters speak.

The day of the race arrived. "I'm surprised you

still want to race!" .... the hare.

"Why? I'm sure to win!" the tortoise ....

The race began and the hare was soon out of sight.

"The tortoise will be miles behind me," the hare

.... to himself. "I'll stop and have

a nap in this nice patch of long grass by the road."

> Don't use the same verb twice. You could use some of the verbs from your table above.

When the tortoise caught up, he found the hare still sleeping in the grass.

"The hare isn't so fast when he's asleep," he .... as he plodded on.

When the hare finally woke up, he saw the tortoise nearing the finish line.

"How did this happen?" he ...., sprinting as fast as he could.

4 What do you think the hare and the tortoise said to each other after the race? Write a conversation between them. Make sure you use correct punctuation and choose suitable verbs to show how the characters speak.

Do you think the hare would apologise to the tortoise?

Would their conversation be friendly or not? Do you think they would joke about the race?

Start a new line when a new character starts speaking.

Would the tortoise be happy that he'd proved his point?

....

....

....

....

....

....

....

....

★ **Extra Challenge**

Look up the fable 'The Fox and the Crow'. Once you've read it, rewrite the fable using direct speech.

....

....

"I can use direct speech in my writing."

First Day at School

When you're describing characters, it's a good idea to include plenty of detail. This will help the reader to imagine what the character looks like and also tell them about the character's personality.

Noun phrases and adverbials are two ways of adding detail to your descriptions.

Key Terms

- A <u>noun phrase</u> is a group of words which contains a noun and any words that describe the noun. Noun phrases can be expanded by adding extra detail.

  e.g. the banana is a noun phrase
  e.g. the mouldy brown banana in the fruit bowl is an expanded noun phrase

- An <u>adverbial</u> is a word or group of words which describes a verb. It can describe why, when, where or how often something happens.

  e.g. I stayed inside because of the snow.
  e.g. They put the pie on the table.
  e.g. Every Monday, I play board games.

1 The pictures below show two characters from a story set in a school. Write two noun phrases to describe each character. Try to make your noun phrases as interesting as possible. The first one has been done for you.

1. the hard-working pupil with a pink pencil

2. ....

1. ....

2. ....

2 These sentences are from the start of the story. Rewrite each sentence, expanding the underlined noun phrases.

> Noun phrases add detail to your descriptions — this helps the reader to imagine your characters.

The teacher showed Amal to her seat next to a girl.

....

....

The girl, who had brown hair and

green eyes, turned to greet Amal.

....

....

....

....

3 Rewrite these sentences from the story, adding an adverbial to each one. You can use the adverbials in the box below to help you.

> Do the adverbials you've chosen make Marie seem friendly or unfriendly? Would she seem different if you used different adverbials?

The girl told Amal that her name was Marie.

....

....

She began to tell Amal all about her summer holidays.

....

....

In a bored voice,   With a welcoming grin,

Smiling warmly,   while glaring angrily at her desk

as soon as Amal sat down   In a cheerful voice,

4 In the next part of the story, Amal meets the school's headmaster. Continue the story, using noun phrases and adverbials to make it as descriptive as possible. You can use the picture and hints below to help you.

Does the headmaster look friendly or scary?

You could use noun phrases to describe how the headmaster looks.

You could use adverbials to describe how he speaks and moves.

You could describe what the headmaster is wearing — use noun phrases to make your description detailed.

....

....

....

....

....

....

★ Extra Challenge

Write a description of a member of your family. Use noun phrases and adverbials to make it as detailed as possible.

....

....

....

"I can use noun phrases and adverbials in my writing."

The Magic Pebble

Effective descriptions help to make stories interesting to read because they bring the settings and characters to life. You can make your descriptions more effective by using a variety of different adverbs and adjectives.

Grammar Guide

- A <u>noun</u> is a word that names something.   e.g. the duck
- An <u>adjective</u> describes a noun.   e.g. the talented duck
- A <u>verb</u> is a doing or being word.   e.g. The talented duck danced.
- An <u>adverb</u> describes a verb.   e.g. The talented duck danced gracefully.

(1) This extract is from the start of a fantasy story about a magic pebble. Underline all the adverbs in the extract and circle all the adjectives.

Clouds hung menacingly in the black sky as roaring waves crashed against the

tall cliffs. Battling bravely against the strong winds, April glanced towards the

choppy ocean. She noticed a stone glistening strangely on the shoreline.

Pick an adverb or adjective from the extract that you think could be more interesting. Suggest an alternative to replace it with.

Original word: ....

Replacement: ....

Why is your replacement more effective?

‖‖‖‖‖‖‖‖‖‖‖‖‖‖‖‖‖‖‖‖‖‖‖‖‖‖‖
Think about how the original word and the replacement make you feel.
‖‖‖‖‖‖‖‖‖‖‖‖‖‖‖‖‖‖‖‖‖‖‖‖‖‖‖

....

....

Section 3 — Writing Fiction

2) Add adverbs and adjectives to complete the extract below. Make sure you choose interesting words.

Despite the .... storm, April paused. She peered

.... through the .... rain.

She knew she should get home as

quickly as possible, but she couldn't

resist the .... pebble.

..............................., she began

making her way to the shoreline.

3) Read the next part of the story. Rewrite the extract, replacing the highlighted adverbs and adjectives with more interesting ones in order to make the description more vivid.

Slowly, April clambered over the **sharp** rocks, edging closer to the **strange** pebble. She had almost reached it when she saw a **strange** figure **quickly** approaching. Wearing an **old** hat and a **big** cloak, the figure was soon beside her. A **nice** smile spread **slowly** across his **nice** face.

....

....

....

....

....

....

4 Here is the next part of the story. Finish rewriting the extract, adding adverbs and adjectives to make it as interesting as possible.

The stranger pointed at the stone. April reached out and wrapped her fingers around it. Lightning flashed across the sky. Thunder roared in April's ears and the ground began to spin. Then, there was stillness. Everything had changed.

The cloaked stranger pointed insistently at the glowing stone. ....

....

....

....

....

....

★ **Extra Challenge**

Talk about your work with a partner. Have you added different words? How does their version make you feel?

5 Continue the story, using adverbs and adjectives to describe the place where April finds herself.

You can choose your own setting or use this picture for inspiration.

....

....

....

....

....

....

....

"I can use adverbs and adjectives to make my writing more interesting."

The Missing Scone

When the reader feels uncertain about what's going to happen next, it makes the story more exciting for them. This is called building suspense.

Choosing verbs and adverbs carefully, withholding information and using short sentences are all techniques you can use to build suspense.

Key Terms

A <u>verb</u> is a doing or being word.

An <u>adverb</u> describes a verb.

<u>Short sentences</u> break up the action and help to build suspense.

When you <u>withhold information</u>, you don't tell the reader every detail. This makes them want to find out what happens next.

e.g. Claude washed the car.

e.g. Claude washed the car thoroughly.

e.g. The floorboards creaked. Claude paused. He crept forward.

e.g. Claude peered round the door. It was there, the thing he had been searching for, staring back at him.

1 This is an extract from a mystery story about a scone that goes missing. Read the extract and then answer the question that follows.

Gabby sighed heavily — she was exhausted. After hours of searching, she was still no closer to finding the culprit. As she turned back towards the doorway, something caught her eye. She gasped. Her heart racing, she strode across the kitchen and knelt down.

Her face glowed with excitement. She'd finally made a discovery.

The writer doesn't tell you anything about what Gabby has discovered. Explain how this made you feel when you were reading the extract.

....

....

2 After making her discovery, Gabby decides to set a trap for the thief. Circle the word from each pair that will create the most suspense in the extract.

Gabby knew that she needed to be as quiet as possible. She **dumped / placed** the bait on the table, then **tiptoed / stomped** to the pantry. She closed the door **silently / loudly** behind her and waited. After just a few moments, she heard a **mysterious / familiar** tapping.

Gabby nudged the door open just a crack and peered **anxiously / casually** into the kitchen. There was something there. She tried to stay silent, but she was breathing **calmly / heavily** and her hands had started shaking **uncontrollably / slightly**.

3 Read the next part of the story. Fill in the gaps with your own verbs and adverbs to create as much suspense as possible.

> Remember to choose your verbs and adverbs carefully. Make sure they're interesting and effective.

Without making a sound, Gabby .... inched the pantry door open further. This was her chance. She .... into the kitchen. The intruder was sitting with his back to her. She crawled .... across the floor. Just as she was about to reach him, he .... away from her and .... towards the back door. Quick as a flash, Gabby .... after him, but he'd already disappeared through the cat flap.

4 Using short sentences is another way of building suspense. Rewrite the passage below so that it uses shorter sentences.

You can change the wording of the extract or leave bits out if you want to.

Gabby raced outside and began searching in the bushes.

Suddenly, she paused because she could hear a rustling noise coming from the flowerbed behind her.

....

....

....

....

★ **Extra Challenge**

Write the end of the story. Does Gabby manage to catch the culprit in the garden?

5 Here is the start of a paragraph about Gorka, who finds a mysterious box in his attic. Continue the paragraph, creating as much suspense as possible.

Gorka studied the box for a moment, then placed it on his desk. ....

....

....

....

....

....

....

....

You could withhold information about what is in the box.

Remember to use short sentences.

"I can build suspense in my writing."

Section 3 — Writing Fiction   *© CGP — not to be photocopied*

The Mysterious Island

Adventure stories often include lots of action to make them exciting to read. One way to add action to your stories is to create situations where your characters are in physical danger and then describe how they escape.

(1) Dawud and his dog, Scamps, are the main characters in a story about a mysterious island. Each pair of sentences below describes two events that could happen in the story. For each pair, colour in the most exciting event.

Dawud finds an old boot in the Lost Palace.

Scamps sets off a booby trap in the Lost Palace.

Dawud is trapped in a treacherous maze in the Lost Palace's dungeons.

Dawud decides not to visit the dungeons of the Lost Palace.

They have a picnic in Crossbones Forest.

They are chased by a tiger in Crossbones Forest.

As Dawud and Scamps are crossing the old rope bridge, it starts to fall apart.

They throw sticks into the river from the old rope bridge.

Dawud and Scamps are caught in a whirlpool.

Dawud and Scamps go swimming in a lake.

They walk along the beach and find some shells.

They are trapped in some quicksand on the beach.

Section 3 — Writing Fiction

2 Look at the map of the mysterious island below. There are four locations marked on the map. Write down something exciting that might happen to Dawud and Scamps in each location.

1. Monster Reef
2. Crystal Cliffs
3. Zigzag Mountain
4. The Forbidden Cave

1. ....

2. ....

3. ....

4. ....

3 In the next part of the story, Dawud and Scamps cross the Whistling Valley. Fill in the gap in the extract, adding some action to make it more exciting.

The uneven path wound steeply upwards. Dawud and Scamps

walked slowly, being careful not to trip on the sharp rocks.

What dangers might Dawud and Scamps find in the Whistling Valley?

....

....

....

....

....

Exhausted, they trudged on until they reached the shore of the Lava Lake.

(4) Continue the story by describing what happens to Dawud and Scamps at the Lava Lake. Include as much action as possible. You can use the picture and hints below to help you.

What is the dangerous situation Dawud and Scamps find themselves in?

Are there any dangerous animals in the lake?

Do they have to cross the Lava Lake? How do they manage to get across safely?

Do they nearly fall into the Lava Lake? Or are they attacked?

....

....

....

....

....

....

....

....

⭐ Extra Challenge

Finish the story, describing how Dawud and Scamps escape from the mysterious island.

....

....

"I can add action to make my writing exciting."

Answers

Pages 3-5 — Planning Your Writing

1. You should have coloured these boxes blue:
   - A script for a school play about a daring pirate adventure
   - A fantasy story about a mischievous elf who tricks humans
   - A poem about a day at the circus
   - A mystery story about the case of Mrs Simm's stolen wheelbarrow

   You should have coloured these boxes red:
   - An article explaining new train ticket prices in the region
   - An explanation in a textbook about how waterfalls form
   - Instructions on how to get to the city centre from the airport

2. Any suitable answer. For example:

   I think that extract **2** was written for adults because **it uses formal language and longer sentences**.

3. You should have matched the texts like this:
   - A leaflet encouraging children to walk to school — Persuasive language, commands
   - A mystery story set on a deserted island — Language that builds suspense, short sentences
   - A diary entry about what you did at the weekend — First person, chatty language

   You should have circled 'Serious tone' and 'Facts and figures'.

4. You should have circled:

   Around AD 790, ships full of raiding warriors landed on British shores. The Vikings had arrived.

   You should have put the topics in this order:

   What did the Vikings do while they were in Britain? — **2**

   Why did the Vikings first come to Britain? — **1**

   When and why did the Vikings leave? — **3**

5. Any suitable plan for the story. For example:

   1. Beginning — Scott volunteers to take part in a trick at a magic show.

   2. The spell goes wrong! He can no longer speak, but only ribbit like a frog.

   3. Desperate for a cure, he goes to visit a mysterious old lady who lives in his village.

   4. To reverse the spell he must sit in the village pond for two whole days and nights.

   5. End — The cure works! Scott swears that he'll never go to a magic show again.

Pages 6-7 — Editing Your Work

1. You should have crossed out unnecessary words to avoid repetition. For example:

   The wheel turned ~~slowly~~ as we slowly rose higher above the skyline. There was an amazing view from the top ~~and it was incredible~~! I could see people in the streets scurrying around like ants ~~in the streets~~. My mum took lots of photos, so I brought some ~~photos my mum took~~ into school to show my friends.

2. Any suitable rewriting of the extracts that makes them flow better. For example:
   - The soldier had been marching for hours. He was tired and sore. He wanted to rest but he still had miles to go.
   - He had blisters on his toes and heels.

3. Any suitable rewriting that uses the suggestions to make the extract better. For example:

   Monty crept silently towards the unicorn. Suddenly, it bolted into the forest, leaving a trail of glitter behind it. Monty sprinted through the trees, desperately trying to keep up. Eventually, exhaustion forced him to stop. He watched as the unicorn vanished into the darkness.

4. Any sensible suggestions. For example:
   - Avoiding repetition of the word 'litter'.
   - Combining the first two sentences.
   - 'or they can get stuck in it' isn't needed.
   - Breaking up the final sentence.

Page 8 — Proofreading Your Work

1. These are the errors you should have marked and corrected in the text:

   The snow leopard is a species of large cat that are (is) found in Asia. It lives in mountainous areas like the Himalayas, where the landscape is **rockey (rocky)** and the temperature is **well (very)** low. Snow **leopads (leopards)** have thick fur to keep them warm and their patterned coat allows them to blend in with **there (their)** surroundings. They

Answers

also have big **fury (furry)** paws that help them to walk on snow. Unlike lions and tigers**. (,)** snow leopards can't **raw (roar)** — instead, they communicate in hisses and growls**? (.)**

Unfortunately, there **were (are)** lots of threats to snow leopards. Global warming is changing their habitat**: (,)** making it difficult for them to find food. In addition, they are often hunted for their **beautyful (beautiful)** coats. However, there is hope for the species. Many countries in Asia are trying to save the snow leopard by protecting **it's (its)** habitat and educating the public.

Pages 9-11 — A Letter to a Friend

1. You should have sorted the examples into the following groups:

Formal	Informal
Dear Sir	See you soon
Yours faithfully	Loads of love
To whom it may	Hi
concern	Love and hugs
Best regards	Hello
Yours sincerely	

2. You should have coloured these sentences red:
   - We took tonnes of great photos!
   - It was boiling — we couldn't believe how sunny it was.
   - The country roads were well bumpy.

   You should have coloured these sentences blue:
   - I went on a bicycle ride with my friends.
   - We paused to enjoy some delicious snacks.
   - I am disappointed that you were unable to attend.

3. You should have underlined the following:

   My **mother informed me** that you **will be visiting us** next month. I am **extremely** excited about seeing you. We can go on an **excursion** to the new theme park in my area. I have heard that it is **thoroughly enjoyable**, **despite** the queues for the rides being **rather long**. We may also **travel** into the city **in order to visit** the shoe shop **I was speaking to you about**. Recently, **I purchased** some **wellington boots** there.

   Any suitable rewriting of the extract that uses informal language. For example:

   My mum told me that you're coming to visit next month. I'm so excited about seeing you. We can go on a day trip to the new theme park in

my area. I've heard that it's really fun, even though the queues for the rides are very long. We could also go into the city so we can visit the shoe shop I was telling you about. Recently, I bought some wellies there.

4. Your writing should have a friendly, personal tone, and you should have used features of informal writing. For example:
   - You should have used an appropriate greeting and sign-off, e.g. 'Hi Granny', 'Lots of love'.
   - You should have written in the first person, e.g. '**We're** having a great time here in Venice — **I've** never eaten so much ice cream in all **my** life!'
   - You should have used chatty, informal language, e.g. 'The weather has been **fab**, so I'm **really gutted** that I forgot to pack my sunglasses.'

Pages 12-14 — A Day at a Country Show

1. You should have filled the gaps like this:

   Last weekend, I went to a country show in Somerset. We **arrived** a bit late, so I **had** to hurry to get to the first event — the children's show jumping competition. I **ran** to the arena and **found** a seat just in time. I **was** so excited that I **held** my breath as the first pony **trotted** into the arena.

2. You should have rewritten the extract like this:

   I'd never seen a bird of prey up close before. **I** held the owl gently on **my** arm as she peered at **me** with her bright orange eyes. **I** was quite scared at first, but **I** was proud of **myself** for staying calm.

3. You should have rewritten the sentences in this order:

   After seeing the birds of prey, I took part in the custard pie-throwing contest. Then, I washed the custard off my face and went to watch the tractor race. Later, I went to the results ceremony for the giant vegetable competition — it was the perfect way to end the day.

4. You should have written a clear, well-structured description of how you learned the skill, using these techniques:
   - You should have written about your experience in the first person, e.g. 'Last year,

Answers

my mum said that I could start taking piano lessons.'

- You should have used the past tense to describe your experience, e.g. 'My teacher **told** me the names of the notes and **taught** me what different musical symbols mean.'

- You should have put the steps in the process in chronological order, e.g. '**After** my teacher had explained how to read music, I learned to play my first tune. **When I got home**, I practised it for an hour.'

Pages 15-17 — My Recipe Book

1. The correct order is 5, 2, 6, 4, 1, 3.

   Any sensible steps, for example:

   - Make some icing to stick the cakes together.
   - Spread icing on the top of each cake.

2. Any suitable answers. For example:

   For this recipe you'll need 120ml of double cream and 220g of chocolate (**you can use dark or milk chocolate**).
   Bring the cream to the boil — **be careful not to let it burn**.
   Pour the hot cream over the chocolate and stir **until the mixture is smooth**.

3. Any sensible instructions, for example:
   1. Measure out the ingredients using some weighing scales.
   2. Put the butter and icing sugar into a mixing bowl.
   3. Use a wooden spoon to beat the mixture.

4. You should have written a clear and detailed set of instructions about how to make the sandwich. For example:

   - You should have written your points in a logical order, e.g. 'Take a bread roll and cut it in half. **Then**, spread a thin layer of butter on each half of the roll.'

   - You should have added extra details to make each step easier to understand, e.g. 'Next, cut some cherry tomatoes in half — **you'll need about seven tomatoes**. Finally, add a slice of cheese (**you can use whichever cheese is your favourite**).'

Pages 18-20 — How Butterflies Develop

1. You should have matched up:

   Butterfly eggs are often round. — although — They can also be shaped like cylinders.

   You have to look carefully to find butterfly eggs. — because — They are extremely small.

   Different butterflies always choose certain plants. — when — They are deciding where to lay their eggs.

   The eggs remain on the plant. — until — They are ready to hatch.

2. You should have circled the following linking words:

   The butterfly egg eventually hatches a couple of weeks or months **after** it was laid. However, you'll be disappointed **if** you were expecting a butterfly to emerge from the egg. Instead, it is a caterpillar that crawls free. The caterpillar begins to eat the plants around it **as soon as** it hatches. It grows very quickly **because** it eats such a huge amount. In fact, a caterpillar grows so fast **that** it has to shed its skin several times throughout its life.

3. Any suitable fronted adverbials. For example:

   When it is fully grown, a caterpillar turns into a pod-like structure called a cocoon. **Inside the cocoon**, it gradually transforms into a colourful butterfly. **Several weeks later**, the butterfly crawls free.

4. You should have written a detailed explanation of how a dragon develops, using varied sentence structures. For example:

   - You should have written a step-by-step explanation of the life cycle. You could have started with the dragon egg stage, e.g. 'When it is laid, the dragon's egg lies in the nest for seven months.'

   - You could then have moved on to the baby dragon stage of the life cycle, e.g. 'After seven months, the egg cracks and a baby dragon hatches.'

   - You should have used linking words to add detail to your writing, e.g. 'The baby dragon must practise daily **until** it has learned to growl convincingly.'

Answers

- You should also have used fronted adverbials to vary your sentence structure, e.g. **'Fifteen years later,** the baby dragon will become a teenager.'

Pages 21-23 — Save Our Playground!

1. You should have underlined one of these statements in blue:
   - Everyone knows how important the playground is to our community.
   - the local council are planning to close it.
   - Hundreds of families enjoy the playground every week.
   - It's a popular and friendly place for children to have fun.

   You should have underlined one of these rhetorical questions in green:
   - Isn't that ridiculous?
   - Where else will they play?
   - What about their safety and happiness?

   You should have underlined one of these commands in red:
   - Sign our petition today to help prevent this happening!
   - Help us fight this terrible proposal.
   - Make your voice heard!

2. Any suitable rhetorical questions. For example:
   Isn't it time to put a stop to this plan?
   Shouldn't children be encouraged to play outside?
   Who can deny that the playground is a great place for children to exercise?

3. Any suitable commands. For example:
   Tell all your friends about our campaign.
   Write to the council and complain.
   Come to the community meeting next week.

4. Your article should use persuasive techniques to convince people to vote for you. For example:
   - You should have used statements to put forward your argument, e.g. 'This school needs a councillor who is committed to making things better for all pupils.'
   - You should have used rhetorical questions to make your reader think, e.g. 'Don't you wish we had better sports equipment?'
   - You should have used commands, e.g. 'Vote for me in the council elections!'

Pages 24-26 — Summer Holidays

1. You should have coloured these boxes red:
   - Fields lay like a patchwork quilt as far as the eye could see.
   - Cooped up in the car, I grew as restless as a storm.
   - The traffic was crawling along like an exhausted tortoise.

   You should have coloured these boxes blue:
   - The road was a ribbon stretching out into the distance.
   - It was the hottest day of the year and the car was a furnace.
   - The picnic basket was a treasure chest of delicious snacks.

2. Any suitable similes. For example:
   - The sea was as **blue** as **the summer sky**.
   - The rocks were as **sharp** as **dragons' teeth**.
   - The path wound up the hill like **a slithering snake**.

3. You should have underlined these descriptions which appeal to the senses:
   The **birds were chirping** as I set out. The breeze **swept across my face**, **ruffling my hair** and carrying with it the **sweet smell of wild flowers**. **Mud squelched** under my boots as I made my way into the woods. I paused for a moment, **running my hands over the rough, gnarled bark** of a tree and **listening to its leaves rustling** above me.

4. Any suitable words or phrases which appeal to the senses. For example:
   Floating on my back, I listened to the **happy** sound of **other children laughing and splashing** all around me. I swam closer to the shore. Beneath the water, I could feel **strands of slimy seaweed tickling my legs**.

5. You should have written a vivid description that helps the reader imagine what your favourite place is like. Here are some techniques you could have used:
   - Similes to make your setting come to life, e.g. 'The theme park is like a whirlwind of energy and excitement.'
   - Metaphors to make your description more effective, e.g. 'The rollercoasters are eagles, soaring and swooping through the air.'

46

Answers

- Language which appeals to the senses to help the reader imagine the scene, e.g. 'My ears sting with the screams of excited laughter and the roar of carriages whooshing overhead.'

Pages 27-29 — The Hare and the Tortoise

1. Any suitable suggestions. For example:

   The hare was watching the tortoise amble along. He couldn't believe how slowly the tortoise moved. "**I've never seen anyone move so slowly in all of my life**," he teased.

   The tortoise knew he wasn't that slow. He thought of a way to prove it. "**We should have a race — I'm not as slow as you think**," he suggested confidently.

   "**Alright, let's race! Of course, there's no chance you'll beat me!**" laughed the hare.

2. Any suitable verbs. For example:
   - happily — giggled, chortled, laughed
   - sadly — wailed, cried, howled
   - softly — muttered, mumbled, whispered
   - loudly — yelled, bellowed, shouted

3. Any suitable verbs. For example:

   The day of the race arrived. "I'm surprised you still want to race!" **laughed** the hare.

   "Why? I'm sure to win!" the tortoise **insisted**.

   The race began and the hare was soon out of sight.

   "The tortoise will be miles behind me," the hare **grinned** to himself. "I'll stop and have a nap in this nice patch of long grass by the road."

   When the tortoise caught up, he found the hare still sleeping in the grass. "The hare isn't so fast when he's asleep," he **chuckled** as he plodded on.

   When the hare finally woke up, he saw the tortoise nearing the finish line. "How did this happen?" he **wailed**, sprinting as fast as he could.

4. Your conversation should use direct speech and a variety of different verbs.
   - You should have used the correct punctuation, e.g. **"**I'm sorry,**"** muttered the hare**,** **"**I shouldn't have teased you.**"**
   - You should have used suitable verbs to show how the characters are speaking, e.g. "It's alright," **smiled** the tortoise. "I expect you'll pace yourself better next time we race!"

Pages 30-32 — First Day at School

1. Any suitable noun phrases. For example:
   - the long-haired girl with a thoughtful expression
   - the smiley girl with her hair in a bun
   - the friendly child with diamond earrings

2. Any suitable expansion of the noun phrases. For example:
   - **The welcoming teacher** showed Amal to her seat next to **a tall girl with a stack of books on her desk**.
   - The girl, who had **long, brown, plaited hair** and **sparkling green eyes**, turned to greet Amal.

3. Any suitable rewriting of the sentences to add adverbials. For example:
   - **Smiling warmly,** the girl told Amal that her name was Marie.
   - **In a cheerful voice,** she began to tell Amal all about her summer holidays.

4. You should have written a detailed description that helps the reader to imagine the headmaster. For example:
   - You should have used noun phrases to add detail to your sentences, e.g. '**A black hat with a ridiculously large tassel** was jammed on top of **his thick, greasy, grey hair**.'
   - You should have included a variety of adverbials, e.g. '**Fixing Amal with a stern glare,** he introduced himself as Mr Strubkins.'

Pages 33-35 — The Magic Pebble

1. You should have underlined these adverbs: menacingly, bravely, strangely

   You should have circled these adjectives: black, roaring, tall, strong, choppy

   Any suitable selection and alternative. For example:

   Original word: tall

   Replacement: towering

   Any suitable explanation. For example:

   My replacement gives the reader a better idea of the size of the cliffs, which makes them seem more threatening.

Answers

Answers

2. Any suitable adverbs and adjectives.
For example:

Despite the **dreadful** storm, April paused. She peered **eagerly** through the **pouring** rain. She knew she should get home as quickly as possible, but she couldn't resist the **gleaming** pebble. **Cautiously**, she began making her way to the shoreline.

3. Any suitable rewriting of the extract.
For example:

Gingerly, April clambered over the **jagged** rocks, edging closer to the **peculiar** pebble. She had almost reached it when she saw a **mysterious** figure **hastily** approaching. Wearing an **ancient** hat and an **enormous** cloak, the figure was soon beside her. A **warm** smile spread **gently** across his **friendly** face.

4. Any suitable rewriting of the extract that includes descriptive adverbs and adjectives.
For example:

The cloaked stranger pointed insistently at the glowing stone. April reached out **nervously** and wrapped her **trembling** fingers around it. Lightning flashed **fiercely** across the **inky** sky. Thunder roared **viciously** in April's ears and the ground began to spin **furiously**. Then, there was **absolute** stillness. Everything had changed **completely**.

5. You should have written a vivid description of the new setting. For example:

• You should have used adjectives to make your writing more detailed and interesting, e.g. 'April squinted in the **dazzling** sunshine. **Dense**, **tropical** rainforest had replaced the **blustery** beach.'

• You should have included adverbs to make your writing more effective, e.g. 'The waterfall crashed **powerfully** into the pool below.'

Pages 36-38 — The Missing Scone

1. Any sensible answer. For example:

• Curious, because I wanted to find out more about what Gabby had discovered.

• Excited, because I wanted to know what Gabby had found.

• Anxious, because I wasn't sure what was going to happen next.

2. You should have circled these words:
Gabby knew that she needed to be as quiet as possible. She **placed** the bait on the table, then **tiptoed** to the pantry. She closed the door **silently** behind her and waited. After just a few moments, she heard a **mysterious** tapping. Gabby nudged the door open just a crack and peered **anxiously** into the kitchen. There was something there. She tried to stay silent, but she was breathing **heavily** and her hands had started shaking **uncontrollably**.

3. Any suitable verbs and adverbs which create suspense. For example:

Without making a sound, Gabby **gently** inched the pantry door open further. This was her chance. She **crept** into the kitchen. The intruder was sitting with his back to her. She crawled **stealthily** across the floor. Just as she was about to reach him, he **leapt** away from her and **sprinted** towards the back door. Quick as a flash, Gabby **dived** after him, but he'd already disappeared through the cat flap.

4. Any suitable rewriting of the extract which uses shorter sentences. For example:
Gabby raced outside. She began searching in the bushes. Suddenly, she paused. She could hear a rustling noise. It was coming from the flowerbed behind her.

5. Your writing should create plenty of suspense so that the reader is uncertain about what will happen next. For example:

• You should have chosen your verbs and adverbs carefully to build suspense, e.g. 'Gorka **clawed impatiently** at the clasp on the box.'

• You should have used short sentences to break up the action, e.g. 'He heard a click. The lid flew open.'

• You could have withheld information from the reader, e.g. 'Gorka gasped. It was dazzling! He'd never seen anything like it.'

Pages 39-41 — The Mysterious Island

1. You should have coloured in these events:

• Scamps sets off a booby trap in the Lost Palace.

• Dawud is trapped in a treacherous maze in the Lost Palace's dungeons.

Answers

- They are chased by a tiger in Crossbones Forest.
- As Dawud and Scamps are crossing the old rope bridge, it starts to fall apart.
- Dawud and Scamps are caught in a whirlpool.
- They are trapped in some quicksand on the beach.

2. Any suitable exciting events. For example:

   1. Monster Reef: An ocean serpent tries to eat them.
   2. Crystal Cliffs: They find a jewel which turns Scamps into a monkey.
   3. Zigzag Mountain: They have to escape from the maze of the mountain demons.
   4. The Forbidden Cave: They disturb a colony of giant bats, who chase them out of the cave.

3. Any suitable action that makes the extract more exciting. For example:

   Suddenly, part of the path crumbled beneath their feet and Dawud fell onto a ledge below. He scrabbled helplessly at the cliff face as rocks came tumbling towards him. Scamps grabbed a tree vine and threw it over the edge. His heart pounding, Dawud seized the vine and started to climb. After what seemed like hours, he managed to scramble back up to Scamps.

4. Your writing should include plenty of action to make it exciting for the reader. For example:

   - You should have put the characters in a risky situation, e.g. 'Dawud gulped. The boiling hot lava was bubbling and spitting fiercely.'
   - You should have included some danger, e.g. 'Scamps leapt to the next stepping stone. As he landed, his paws slipped, leaving him teetering on the edge of the rock. Suddenly, a fiery serpent emerged from the lava, hissing viciously.'
   - You should have described how the characters escape from the danger, e.g. 'Dawud, who was a couple of stones behind Scamps, bounded forward. He took the water bottle from his rucksack and splashed its contents in the serpent's face. The serpent recoiled for a moment, giving Dawud time to grab Scamps and hurry on to the next stepping stone.'